Maths

The 11+
10-Minute Tests

For the CEM (Durham University) test

Book 2

Ages
10-11

Practise • Prepare • Pass

Everything your child needs for 11+ success

How to use this book

This book is made up of 10-minute tests and puzzle pages.
There are answers and detailed explanations in the pull-out section at the back of the book.

10-Minute Tests

- There are 31 tests in this book, each containing 12 questions.

- Each test is designed to cover a good range of the question styles and topics that your child could come across in the maths section of their 11+ test, at the same difficulty level.

- Your child should aim to score around 10 or 11 out of 12 in each 10-minute test.
  If they score less than this, use their results to work out the areas they need more practice on.

- If your child hasn't managed to finish the test in time, they need to work on increasing their speed, whereas if they have made a lot of mistakes, they need to work more carefully.

- Keep track of your child's scores using the progress chart on the inside back cover of the book.

Puzzle Pages

- There are 6 puzzle pages in this book, which are a great break from test-style questions.
  They encourage children to practise the same skills that they will need in the test,
  but in a fun way.

Published by CGP

Editors:
Emily Forsberg, Sharon Keeley-Holden, Dawn Wright

With thanks to Alison Griffin and Andy Park for the proofreading.

Please note that CGP is not associated with CEM or The University of Durham in any way.
This book does not include any official questions and it is not endorsed by CEM or The University of Durham.
CEM, Centre for Evaluation and Monitoring, Durham University and *The University of Durham*
are all trademarks of The University of Durham.

ISBN: 978 1 78294 762 2
Printed by Elanders Ltd, Newcastle upon Tyne
Clipart from Corel®

Based on the classic CGP style created by Richard Parsons.

Contents

You have **10 minutes** to do this test. Work as quickly and accurately as you can.

Five people took part in a long-jump competition.
The distances they jumped are recorded in the table below.

Adam	Bing	Cho	Dave	Emma
4.35 m	3.97 m	4.32 m	4.20 m	4.02 m

1.   Who jumped the second longest distance? Circle the correct option.

   A   Adam   **C**   Cho   **E**   Emma
   B   Bing   **D**   Dave

2.   Give the distance Emma jumped in millimetres.

 mm

3.   A regular pentagon is cut along the dotted line shown.
     Two identical new shapes are produced.

   How many obtuse angles are there in one of the new shapes?

4.   Kailash has £43.90. He then gets paid £27.63 and wins £75 in a poetry
     competition. How much money does he have now?

£

2

5. Tina visited six different supermarkets and wrote down the price of 1 kg of pears in each one. The prices are listed below.

    97p, £1.03, £1.20, £1.25, £1, £1.15

    Calculate the mean price of 1 kg of pears.

6. There is normally 400 g of mushrooms in a pack. A special offer pack of mushrooms has 20% extra free. What is the mass of the special offer pack?

     g

7. Film A was made in the year MCMLXXV.
    Film B was made in the year MCMLXXXIV.
    How many years after Film A was Film B made? Circle the correct option.

    A 11   **C** 9   **E** 15
    B 10   **D** 4

Lucas asks everyone in Year 6 where they would like to go on a trip.
He makes a pie chart of the results.

8. What fraction of the children said they wanted to go to either the farm or the zoo? Circle the correct option.

    A $\frac{2}{5}$ **B** $\frac{4}{9}$ **C** $\frac{5}{9}$ **D** $\frac{1}{3}$ **E** $\frac{2}{7}$

9. 24 children said they wanted to go bowling.
    How many said they wanted to go to the zoo?

10. Mr Smith is knitting a scarf. It takes him $1\frac{1}{2}$ minutes to knit each row.
He starts knitting at 5:15 pm. At what time will he have knitted 60 rows?

 : pm

11. Points A and B are joined with a line on the coordinate grid below.

 = 1 cm²

Point C is added to the grid at (5, 4). It is joined to points A and B.
What is the area of the triangle formed?

cm²

12. The diagram below shows a quadrilateral.
An expression is given for the size of each angle in degrees.

not drawn accurately

Which equation is correct? Circle the correct option.

A $3x + 30x = 360$

B $35x = 360$

C $5x = 180$

D $5x = 330$

E $5x = 390$

/ 12

You have **10 minutes** to do this test. Work as quickly and accurately as you can.

1. John creates a sequence by counting back in steps of 4.
   The first term in his sequence is 100. What will the third term be?

2. Bananas cost 13p each. Chris buys five bananas and pays with a £5 note.
   How much change does he get?

3. What is 56 855 rounded to the nearest 100?

4. Which of the shapes below has exactly one line of symmetry?
   Circle the correct option.

   | A | B | C | D | E |

5. 204 × 7001 = 1 428 204

   What is 2040 × 7.001? Circle the correct option.

   A   14.28204

   B   142.8204

   C   1428.204

   D   14 282.04

   E   142 820.4

Max and Holly attend a holiday club. The percentage of time that they each spend on the different types of activity is shown on the chart below.

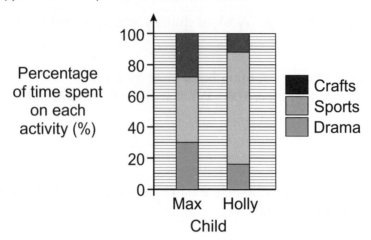

6. What percentage of Holly's time was spent doing sports? Circle the correct option.

   A   30%   C   42%   E   88%

   B   72%   D   66%

7. The children spend $2\frac{1}{2}$ hours at the holiday club.
   How long, in minutes, did Max spend doing drama?

    mins

Aneena is making a path across her garden using square slabs.
The path is one slab wide. This diagram shows the first three slabs she lays.

8. What is the area of one slab? Give your answer in cm².

    cm²

9. The path needs to be 24 m long. How many slabs are needed?

10. A block of ice cream is shown in the diagram below.

5 cm

8 cm

25 cm

Mohammed ate $^1/_4$ of the block of ice cream.
What volume of ice cream did he eat?

 cm³

11. Find the size of angle a, shown in the diagram below.

not drawn accurately

 °

12. Henry has written an expression. When $x = 4$, the value of the expression is 24.
Which of the following could not have been Henry's expression?
Circle the correct option.

    A $x(x + 2)$

    B $^1/_2(x + 11x)$

    C $4x + 8$

    D $8(x - 1)$

    E $5x + 5$

/ 12

You have **10 minutes** to do this test. Work as quickly and accurately as you can.

1.   Which of the shapes below is a regular quadrilateral?
     Circle the correct option.

A   **B**   **C**   **D**   **E**

2.   Mike planted some sunflower seeds on April 29th.
     The shoots appeared on May 4th.
     How many days after planting did the shoots appear?

 days

3.   The graph below shows the changing temperature in a greenhouse one day.

     Use the graph to find the approximate temperature in the greenhouse
     at half past three in the afternoon. Circle the correct option.

     A   12 °C
     B   13 °C
     C   14 °C
     D   16 °C
     E   18 °C

Red pens come in packs of 12 and blue pens come in packs of 20.

4. What is the ratio of red pens in a pack to blue pens in a pack?
   Give your answer in its simplest form.

5. A teacher orders 40 packs of red pens and 9 packs of blue pens.
   How many pens have been ordered in total?

This pictogram shows the number of football cards owned by four children.

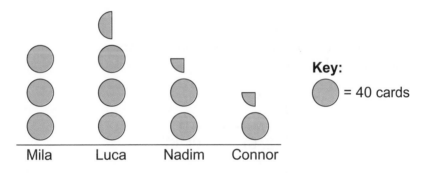

Key:

⬤ = 40 cards

6. Mila gives Nadim some of her cards so that they both have the same number.
   How many cards does Mila have now?

7. What is the mean number of cards owned by the four children?

8. This formula can be used to convert a distance in miles, m, to kilometres, k.

$$k = 8m \div 5$$

Using this formula, convert 20 miles to kilometres.

km

9. Which of the following is not equivalent to the others? Circle the correct option.

  A $^3/_{10}$ of 60
  B 10% of 180
  C $^3/_4$ of 24
  D 0.18 × 1000
  E 5% of 360

10. Linda has 5860 ml of pancake batter. She uses 45 ml of batter to make each pancake. She makes as many pancakes of this size as she can. How much batter is left over?

 ml

The diagram shows the line AB. Line CD is parallel to AB.
Line CD is half as long as line AB.

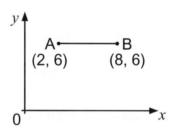

11. Which of these could be the coordinates of C and D? Circle the correct option.

  A C(3, 4) and D(3, 7)   **D** C(4, 4) and D(8, 8)
  B C(2, 4) and D(5, 4)   **E** C(3, 4) and D(6, 1)
  C C(1, 4) and D(7, 4)

12. Line AB is reflected in the *x*-axis, then translated 1 unit left.
    What are the new coordinates of A? Circle the correct option.

  A (2, –5)   **C** (–2, 5)   **E** (–1, –6)
  B (1, –6)   **D** (–3, 6)

/ 12

You have **10 minutes** to do this test. Work as quickly and accurately as you can.

1. Mr Jones puts seven tulips on each table in his restaurant. He has three left over.
    How many tulips could there be in total? Circle the correct option.

    A   60   **C**   56   **E**   11
    B   21   **D**   59

2. It is –18 °C inside a freezer. Its door is left open and the temperature inside
    increases by 5 °C. What is the temperature in the freezer now?

     –☐☐ °C

3. The net below is folded to make a 3D shape.

    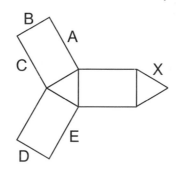

    Which side of the net joins to side X? Circle the correct option.

    A   **B**   **C**   **D**   **E**

4. A ball is dropped onto the ground. The heights of its bounces form a sequence.
    The heights of its first four bounces are shown in the table below.

Bounce 1	Bounce 2	Bounce 3	Bounce 4
40 cm	20 cm	10 cm	5 cm

    What will be the height of its sixth bounce?

    ☐☐.☐☐ cm

11

40 children at a playgroup are given a biscuit and a drink. The children each chose between a chocolate biscuit and a plain biscuit and between juice and milk. The table below shows the number of children who chose each option.

	Juice	Milk	Total
Chocolate		5	9
Plain			
Total	12		40

5. How many children chose a plain biscuit and juice?

6. What percentage of the children chose juice?

%

7. Work out the area of the shape below.

10 cm

6 cm   4 cm   not to scale

18 cm

cm²

8. Noah fills 26 empty jars with homemade jam. An empty jar has a mass of 95 g. Noah puts 450 g of jam into each jar. What is the total mass of the filled jam jars?

g

9. Work out $^2/_5 + ^2/_3$. Circle the correct option.

A $^4/_{15}$ C $1^2/_{15}$ E $2^2/_5$

B $^4/_5$ D $1^1/_{15}$

10. What is the size of angle *b* in the diagram below?

It costs £6 to enter Smashers Pottery Studio. You then pay £3.25 for each plate you paint.

11. Circle the expression that shows the total cost, in pounds, of painting *p* plates.

    A   9.25*p*

    B   6(3.25*p*)

    C   6 + 3.25*p*

    D   6*p* + 3.25

    E   6 − 3.25*p*

12. The graph below shows the cost of painting plates at Plates R Us Pottery Studio.
Plates R Us is free to enter.

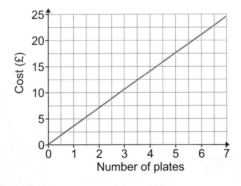

Gina wants to paint ten plates.
How much will she save by going to Plates R Us instead of Smashers?

/ 12

You have **10 minutes** to do this test. Work as quickly and accurately as you can.

1.   A regular pentagon has a perimeter of 600 mm. How long is each side?

 mm

2.   What is 148 979 – 20 072.2?
   Use estimation, then circle the exact answer from these options.

   A   139 456.8

   B   28 029.7

   C   168 906.8

   D   128 906.8

   E   60 610.7

3.   The diameter of a circle is 12.8 cm. What is the radius of the circle?

 cm

4.   Ash has a 7 m wide wall in his bedroom. Ash works out that he can fit four
   different items from those shown below across the wall with no space left over.

bookcase	desk	bed	chair	drawers
1.00 m	2.95 m	2.45 m	1.10 m	0.50 m

   Which item does Ash not use? Circle the correct option.

   A   bookcase   **C**   bed   **E**   drawers

   B   desk   **D**   chair

5. Ruby has $\frac{1}{3}$ of a pizza on her plate. She cuts it into three equal slices.
   What fraction of the whole pizza is each of these three pieces?
   Circle the correct option.

   A $\frac{1}{9}$ **C** $\frac{1}{6}$ **E** $\frac{1}{27}$

   B $\frac{2}{9}$ **D** $\frac{1}{4}$

6. A tent covers a rectangular area of ground measuring 4.32 m by 6 m.
   What area of ground does the tent cover?

 m²

7. This bar chart shows the number of bikes sold in different years by a bike company.

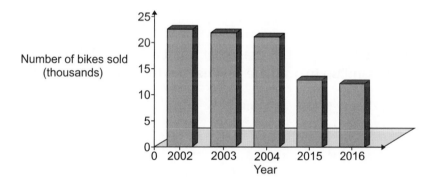

   Why is this bar chart misleading? Circle the correct option.

   A The bars should not be shown as 3D blocks.

   B The bars should be different colours.

   C Some years have been missed out.

   D There is no grid to help you read the values exactly.

   E The scale should go up in ones.

8. A candle is lit at 6:30 pm. It burns at a steady rate and lasts until 8:45 pm.
   At what time had $\frac{1}{5}$ of the candle burned?

   : pm

9. Sarah takes five spelling tests. Her mean mark for the five tests is 7.
She takes a sixth test. Her mean mark for the six tests is 6.
How many marks did she get in the sixth test?

10. Lucy starts at a number and counts up in steps of 8. One of the numbers
she counts is 17. Which of these numbers could she have started at?
Circle the correct option.

    A   −16   **C**   −23   **E**   −1

    B   −17   **D**   −24

11. On a coordinate grid, a coin is placed at point (–2, –1). The coin is then moved
left one square and up two squares. What are the coordinates of the coin now?

12. Omar makes the patterns below out of blocks.

   Pattern 1   Pattern 2   Pattern 3   Pattern 4

Which expression represents the number of blocks in the nth
pattern in the sequence? Circle the correct option.

    A $2n + 1$ **C** $n^2 - 1$ **E** $n^2 + n$

    B $n^2 + 1$ **D** n^2

/ 12

Now for a break from 10-minute tests. Try out your skills on this puzzle.

Pyramid Problem

To be allowed to enter the Great Pyramid of Multiplia without being cursed, explorers must first solve a puzzle.

Each box on the pyramid must hold a number that is a multiple of all the numbers in the circles attached to it. An example mini-pyramid is shown on the right:

Oh, one more thing. You have to use these numbers — use each exactly once.

| 140 | 105 | 6 | 8 | 22 | 57 | 15 | 210 | 84 | 12 |

17

10

You have **10 minutes** to do this test. Work as quickly and accurately as you can.

1. In which of the numbers below does the 7 have the largest value?
    Circle the correct answer.

    A   1 234 567

    B   172.8

    C   10 007

    D   952.7

    E   65 427.99

The quiz scores of four teams are shown on the pictogram below.

Key: = 8 points

2. How many more points did Team D get than Team B?

3. Team E got 30 points. Circle the option which shows Team E's points.

    A   **C**   **E**

    B   **D**

4. A rectangle has a width of 15 cm. Its length is twice its width.
    What is the perimeter of the rectangle?

    cm

18

5. A teacher asks a class to write down as many different ways as they can think of to make the number 24. Jas writes down all the statements below.
    Which one is wrong? Circle this statement.

    A   Square five then subtract one.

    B   Divide 144 by six.

    C   Find five percent of 120.

    D   Multiply eight by three.

    E   Subtract 76 from one hundred.

6. Lia pours out 150 ml of lemonade from a full 2.5 litre bottle.
    How much lemonade is left in the bottle? Circle the correct answer.

    A   1 litre

    B   2.25 litres

    C   2.485 litres

    D   2 litres

    E   2.35 litres

7. Stevie draws the triangle shown below. It has an area of 24 cm².

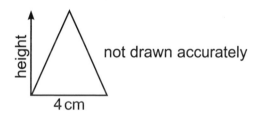

    What is the height of the triangle?

     cm

8. Each letter below is a Roman numeral.

    # I V X L C M

    Find the sum of the numerals shown which have exactly one line of symmetry.
    Write your answer in figures.

9. Find the sum of the two prime numbers between 30 and 40.

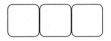

10. Adam collects eggs every day. From Monday to Friday, Adam earns £7.00 per day.
    He earns double this amount per day at the weekend.
    What is the mean amount he earns per day over the full week?

    £

11. Which of the following expressions can be used
    to describe angle b in the diagram?
    Circle the correct option.

    A $360° - a$

    B a

    C $2a$

    D $360° - 2a$

    E $180° - a$

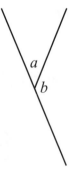

12. The cost, B, in pounds, for each person to attend a board games event can be
    found using the formula $B = (24 \div n) + 2.5$.
    n is the number of people attending the event.
    How much will it cost per person if 10 people attend?

    £

/ 12

You have **10 minutes** to do this test. Work as quickly and accurately as you can.

1.   The number 8 bus always runs exactly on time.
      Part of its timetable is shown below.

Bus Station	Cinema	City Park	High Street	Back Street
1425	1437	1455	1504	1515

Dan is waiting at the High Street stop. It is 2:47 pm.
How long will he have to wait for the number 8 bus?

☐☐ minutes

2.   Which of the following rounds to 20 000?
      Circle the correct answer.

    A   2499 to the nearest 1000.

    B   19 590 to the nearest 100.

    C   19 590 to the nearest 1000.

    D   20 005 to the nearest 10.

    E   20 500 to the nearest 1000.

Jack and Jill are making 3D shapes from coloured cubes.
Each of Jack's cubes has a width of 1 cm.

3.   Jack used six of his cubes to
      make the shape shown here.
      What is the area of the bottom
      face of the shape?

☐☐ cm²

4.   Jill's cubes are 2 cm wide. Jill makes a shape using three of her cubes.
      How many cubes would Jack need to use to make the same shape?

5. What is the remainder when 2576 is divided by 9?

6. Look at the number line below.

What number is the arrow pointing to? Circle the correct answer.

A $2^2/_3$ **B** $^{10}/_3$ **C** $3^3/_4$ **D** $^{13}/_3$ **E** 3

7. Which of the following shapes has the same area as the shape shown below?
Circle the correct option.

A A square, width 5 m
B A rectangle, width 4 m, length 5 m
C A parallelogram, base 7 m, vertical height 3 m
D A triangle, base 10 m, height 4 m
E None of the above

8. Kemi thinks of a number, divides it by 1000 then adds $^1/_4$ to get 5.
What was the number Kemi thought of?

9. Mark says,
"My age lies between the squares of 6 and 7.
It is a prime number, and the digits have a difference of 1."
How old is Mark?

10. The graph below can be used to help convert between miles and kilometres.

Use the graph to convert 25 miles to kilometres.

☐☐☐ km

11. The shape on the right is a kite. Which of the following is true? Circle the correct answer.

not drawn accurately

A $x + y = 60°$

B $x + y = 240°$

C $x + y = 360°$

D $x + y = 120°$

E $x + y = 180°$

12. A number sequence starts on an even number, and its 10th term is odd. Which of the expressions below could be the nth term of this sequence? Circle the correct option.

A $2n$ C n^2 E $n^2 + 1$

B $20 - 2n$ D $2n + 1$

/ 12

You have **10 minutes** to do this test. Work as quickly and accurately as you can.

1. A small packet of popcorn costs 80p. A multipack containing five small packets costs £3.80. How much money is saved by buying a multipack instead of five small packets?

 p

2. The shape below is made from three identical regular hexagons.

not drawn accurately

The perimeter of one hexagon is 36 mm.
What is the perimeter of the shape?

 mm

The shoe sizes of five people are: 7, 3, 5, 2, 4.

3. One of the following statements is not true. Circle this statement.

    A The difference between the largest and smallest shoe sizes is 5.

    B When written in size order, the middle number is 4.

    C The total of the shoe sizes is a prime number.

    D All the shoe sizes are either square or prime numbers.

    E The largest shoe size multiplied by the smallest shoe size is 14.

4. The shoe size of a sixth person is added to the list.
    The mean shoe size of the six people is 5.
    What is the shoe size of the sixth person?

5. Jen makes a sequence of numbers using the following rule to find the next number:
    "Double the previous number and add nine."
    Which of these could be Jen's sequence? Circle the correct answer.

    A 1, 2, 9...   **C** 3, 15, 39...   **E** 1, 10, 29...

    B 1, 11, 22...   **D** 2, 11, 20...

6. A cross and five lines, labelled Q-U, have been
    drawn on the coordinate grid to the right.
    The cross is translated 5 squares up and 2 squares left.
    On which line does the cross now lie?
    Circle the correct option.

    A Line Q

    B Line R

    C Line S

    D Line T

    E Line U

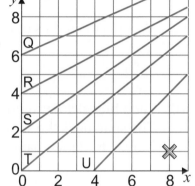

Kate ran to the top of a hill and back down again. The graph below shows
how her height above the bottom of the hill changed during the run.

7. After how many seconds was Kate first halfway up the hill?

 s

8. Last time she ran down the hill, it took her 1 minute 45 seconds.
    How many seconds faster was she this time?

    ☐☐ seconds

Cat has two circular bracelets, as shown below. The smaller bracelet's diameter and circumference are $^2/_3$ of that of the larger bracelet.

75mm

not drawn accurately

9.   What is the radius of the smaller bracelet?

 mm

10. Each bracelet has a number of jewels evenly spaced around the circumference. The spacing is the same on each bracelet. There are 25 jewels in total on both bracelets. How many jewels are on the larger bracelet? Circle the correct answer.

A   5   **B**   10   **C**   15   **D**   17   **E**   20

The ages of two sisters, Abi (aged A) and Bella (aged B) satisfy the equation $2A - 3B = 3$.

11. Which of the following could be Abi and Bella's ages?
     Circle the correct option.

     A   Abi is 4, Bella is 1
     B   Abi is 3, Bella is 2
     C   Abi is 3, Bella is 3
     D   Abi is 3, Bella is 1
     E   Abi is 4, Bella is 2

12. Bella is actually 9 years old. How old is Abi?

/ 12

You have **10 minutes** to do this test. Work as quickly and accurately as you can.

1. What is the size of the acute angle in the diagram?

not drawn accurately

2. Which of the following is an increase in temperature of 10 °C?
    Circle the correct option.

    A   −1 °C to 11 °C

    B   7 °C to −3 °C

    C   −5.9 °C to 6.1 °C.

    D   −5.5 °C to 4.5 °C

    E   −27 °C to −37 °C

Gita is making tea and coffee for a meeting.
The part-filled table below shows the drinks that people have requested.

	With Milk	No Milk	**Total**
Coffee		15	
Tea	13		**29**
Total			**65**

3. How many people wanted coffee with milk?

4. What percentage of people wanted tea with milk?
    Circle the correct option.

    A   2%   **B**   5%   **C**   10%   **D**   20%   **E**   50%

The bar chart below shows the number of people with different hair colours at a party.

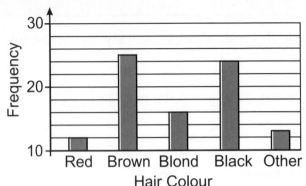

5. What hair colour is twice as common as one of the other colours?
   Circle the correct option.

   A Red   **B** Brown   **C** Blond   **D** Black   **E** Other

6. Why is the bar chart misleading? Circle the correct statement.

   A It doesn't allow for people with grey hair.

   B The vertical axis doesn't increase evenly.

   C The height of the bar for brown hair is not a whole number.

   D The bars should be coloured to match the hair colours.

   E The vertical axis doesn't start at zero.

Jo is following a recipe to make 18 chocolate muffins.
She measures out 450 g of caster sugar into a mixing bowl.

7. What will be the mean amount of caster sugar in each muffin?

   ⬚⬚ g

8. The other ingredients are added to the mixing bowl. The total mass of all the ingredients is 2.5 times the mass of just the sugar. Find the mass of the other ingredients. Give your answer in kilograms.

   ⬚.⬚⬚⬚ kg

9. $\frac{2}{3}x = 90$. What is the value of x?

   ⬚⬚⬚

10. What is the area of the shape below?

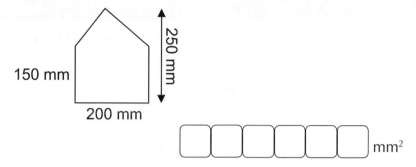

150 mm

250 mm

200 mm

☐☐☐☐☐☐ mm²

11. Which of these is the largest proportion?
    Circle the correct answer.

    A $\frac{1}{4} \times \frac{1}{3}$
    B $\frac{1}{4} + \frac{1}{3}$
    C $\frac{2}{3} - \frac{1}{4}$
    D $\frac{1}{3} \div 4$
    E $\frac{1}{4} \times 3$

12. The first three shapes in a sequence of cubes is shown below.

    Cube 1   Cube 2   Cube 3

    2 cm   3 cm   4 cm

    What is the volume of the 9th cube in the sequence?

    ☐☐☐☐ cm³

/ 12

You have **10 minutes** to do this test. Work as quickly and accurately as you can.

1. Four irregular shapes are shown below.

   Which of the following statements about the four shapes is correct?
   Circle the correct answer.

   A   There are three hexagons and one pentagon.

   B   There are four pentagons.

   C   There are two pentagons and two hexagons.

   D   There are three pentagons and one hexagon.

   E   There are four hexagons.

2. What is the largest factor of 50 that is also a factor of 60?

3. Cheshire cheese is usually priced at £1.50 per 100 g.
   How much would 100 g of Cheshire cheese cost if the
   price was reduced by 10%?

   £

4. A square has a perimeter of 44 cm.
   What is its area in cm²?

    cm²

5. The ruler below shows inches and centimetres.

Use the ruler to estimate the number of inches in one metre,
to the nearest 10 inches. Circle the correct option.

    A   20 inches

    B   40 inches

    C   200 inches

    D   250 inches

    E   400 inches

6. There are fewer than 200 pupils in one year group. The pupils can be split up
into 9 classes, with an equal number of pupils in each class. They can also
be split up into 10 classes, with an equal number of pupils in each class.
What is the largest possible number of pupils in the year group?

The pie chart below shows how 200 people responded when they were asked,
"Do you own a pet?" The angle for the "Yes" sector is 45°.

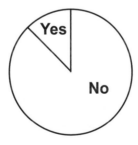

7. Of the people that own a pet, half own a dog.
What fraction of the total own a dog? Circle the correct answer.

    A $\frac{1}{2}$ **B** $\frac{1}{4}$ **C** $\frac{1}{8}$ **D** $\frac{1}{16}$ **E** $\frac{1}{20}$

8. How many people said that they do not own a pet?

9. The diagram below shows a design made up of a circle and some rectangles.

Use the diagram to find the area of the blue rectangle.

 cm²

10. The first four terms in a sequence are 1, 9, 25 and 49.
What is the next term in the sequence?

A point on a grid has coordinates $(x, 2x + 1)$.

11. Which of the points labelled on the grid below could this be?
Give the letter of the correct point.

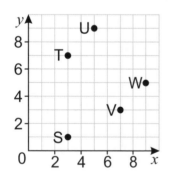

12. The point is translated two squares to the left and one square up.
Which of the following describes the coordinates of the translated point?
Circle the correct option.

A $(x + 1, 2x + 2)$ C $(x - 2, 2x - 1)$ E $(x - 2, 2x + 2)$

B $(x - 1, 2x + 3)$ D $(x + 2, 2x + 2)$

/ 12

Now for a break from 10-minute tests. Try out your skills on these puzzles.

Safe as Houses

Ms Match keeps a spare door key in an electronic safe in the shed.

It is accessed with a 5-digit code. There are no repeated digits in the code. Consecutive numbers, such as 3 and 4, or 8 and 9, are not found next to each other in the code.

If a wrong code is entered, the safe is programmed to give clues. Two attempts to input the code are shown below, with the clues given by the safe.

Key:

○ (top) ○ (bottom)	● (top) ○ (bottom)	● (top) ● (bottom)
Digit not in code	Digit is in code but not in that position	Digit is in code in that position

Can you use the clues to crack the code for the safe?

Interesting Times

All three clocks in Andy's house show different times:

Use these facts to work out the correct time:

- One clock is one minute slow.
- One clock is fifteen minutes slow.
- One clock stopped exactly eleven and a half hours ago.
- It's now afternoon.

You have **10 minutes** to do this test. Work as quickly and accurately as you can.

1. Circle the most likely length of a netball court.

    A   30.5 km   **C**   30.5 cm   **E**   30.5 m²

    B   30.5 mm   **D**   30.5 m

2. What number is the arrow pointing to? Circle the correct answer.

    A   2.51   **B**   2.9   **C**   2.49   **D**   2.48   **E**   2.95

3. An ant is at point A on the coordinate grid below facing north.
   He turns 90° anticlockwise and walks forward two squares.
   Give the coordinates of the ant's new position.

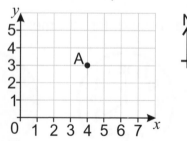

   (☐ , ☐)

4. Lisa and Marc are cycling around a circular track. They leave the start line at the
   same time. Lisa cycles once around the track every $2\frac{1}{2}$ minutes and Marc cycles
   once around the track every 3 minutes. How many minutes will it be before they
   next leave the start line at the same time?

   ☐☐☐ minutes

In a football club there are 40 children. $^1/_5$ of the children are 9 years old, 15% are 10 years old and the rest are 11 years old.

5. How many of the children are 11 years old? Circle the correct answer.

   A 6   **B** 14   **C** 20   **D** 26   **E** 30

6. The football coach wants to draw a pie chart showing the proportions of children of different ages in the club. What angle should the '9 years old' sector have? Circle the correct answer.

   A 72°   **B** 54°   **C** 36°   **D** 15°   **E** 45°

7. A 500 g bag of bird seed costs £1.99. Paul needs 4.5 kg of bird seed. How much will this cost?

   £ ⬜⬜.⬜⬜

8. The perimeter of the rectangular field shown is 44 m.

   12 m

   not drawn accurately

   What is the area of the field?

   ⬜⬜⬜ m²

9. Tom needs 2p coins to play a game at an amusement arcade. He changes two £2 coins and three 20p coins for 2p coins. How many 2p coins does he receive?

   ⬜⬜⬜⬜

10. Jamie says, "I am thinking of two prime numbers that are both less than 20.
If I add them together and double the result, I get 30."
What are the two numbers Jamie is thinking of?

 and

11. Two mothers are comparing the masses of their babies.
Baby Eric is 5.5 pounds and baby Sue is 3.5 kg.

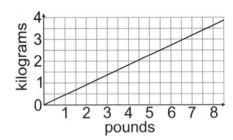

Which statement is true? Circle the correct answer.

   A   Baby Sue is heavier than baby Eric by 2 kg.

   B   Baby Eric is heavier than baby Sue by 1 kg.

   C   Baby Sue is heavier than baby Eric by about 2.25 pounds.

   D   Baby Sue is heavier than baby Eric by exactly 2 pounds.

   E   Baby Eric is heavier than baby Sue by 2.25 pounds.

12. The circumference, C, of a circle with diameter, d, is given by this formula:

$$C = 3.14d$$

What is the circumference of a circle with a diameter of 20 cm?

 cm

/ 12

You have **10 minutes** to do this test. Work as quickly and accurately as you can.

1. What is six million, four hundred and thirty thousand and seventy-two in figures?
    Circle the correct answer.

    A   64 372   **C**   6 043 072   **E**   643 072

    B   6 430 720   **D**   6 430 072

2. Ron is doing a sponsored walk. After walking 8 km, he has done 25% of the walk.
    How long is the walk?

    ☐☐☐ km

In a talent show, children voted for their favourite act. Here is a chart of the results.

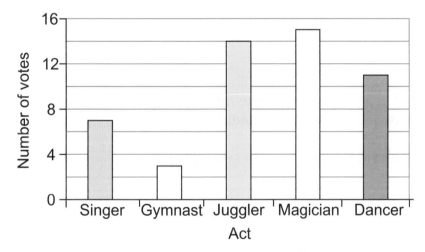

3. Which act got the same number of votes as two other acts combined?
    Circle the correct answer.

    A   Singer   **C**   Juggler   **E**   Dancer

    B   Gymnast   **D**   Magician

4. What is the ratio of votes for the magician to votes for the gymnast?
    Give your answer in its simplest form.

    ☐☐:☐☐

Test 12

5. A spinner numbered 1-10 is shown below.

How many numbers on the spinner are factors of both 24 and 30?

6. Raj makes the sequence of patterns below.

Pattern 1   Pattern 2   Pattern 3   Pattern 4

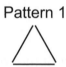

How many lines will there be in Pattern 10?

Andy is taking part in a long-distance bike race. Riders start at 6 am on Monday
and must have finished by 4 pm on Wednesday.

7. How many hours does Andy have to complete the race?

hours

8. Over the first four hours of the race, Andy rode 136 km.
    What was the mean distance he cycled each hour during that part of the race?

km

9. 8 km is approximately 5 miles.
    What is 136 km approximately equal to in miles? Circle the correct answer.

    A   68 miles   C   110 miles   E   211 miles

    B   85 miles   D   150 miles

A rat cage is shown below.

95 cm

141 cm

52 cm

10. What is the area of the floor of the cage?

 cm²

11. Each pet rat needs about 0.07 m³ of cage space. Use estimation to work out how many rats you could keep in this cage. Circle the correct answer.

A 1 **B** 5 **C** 20 **D** 10 **E** 100

12. The graph below shows how y is related to x.

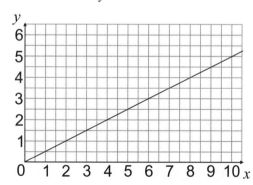

Circle the equation below which shows the same relationship.

A $y = \frac{1}{2}x$

B $y = 2x$

C $y = x + 2$

D $y = x - 2$

E $x = \frac{1}{2}y$

/ 12

You have **10 minutes** to do this test. Work as quickly and accurately as you can.

1. What is the least number of extra squares that must be shaded so that the grid has the two diagonal lines of symmetry shown?

2. Which set of angles could be found inside a parallelogram?
    Circle the correct option.

    A   50°, 60°, 130°, 120°

    B   50°, 50°, 125°, 125°

    C   50°, 50°, 130°, 130°

    D   50°, 50°, 40°, 40°

    E   50°, 60°, 125°, 125°

3. A new pound coin has a thickness of 2.8 mm. An old pound coin has a thickness of 3.15 mm. Sarah builds a tower of 100 new pound coins and a tower of 100 old pound coins. What is the difference in height between the two towers?
    Circle the correct option.

    A   0.35 mm   **C**   3.5 cm   **E**   35 cm

    B   3.5 mm   **D**   0.35 cm

4. Jon makes a scale model of his pet dog, Floppy. The model is 15% of the size of Floppy. If Floppy is 86 cm long, how long will the model be?

     cm

Three identical isosceles triangles are cut from a piece of card, as shown below.

20 cm   not drawn accurately

32 cm

5.   What is the area of one of the triangles?

 cm²

6.   What percentage of the piece of card is left over after all three triangles
      have been cut from it?

 %

The petrol tank in Emily's car holds 72 litres when full.

7.   Petrol costs £1.11 a litre.
      How much does it cost Emily for a full tank of petrol?

£

8.   The diagram shows how much petrol is left in Emily's petrol tank after a journey.

      How many litres of petrol are left in the tank?

 litres

Class 5 are taking part in a readathon lasting seven weeks. The total number of books read since the start of the readathon is recorded at the end of each week, as shown in the graph.

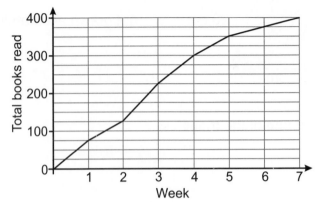

9.   How many books were read during the second week? Circle the correct answer.

    A   25   **C**   75   **E**   40

    B   50   **D**   125

10.   There are 30 children in Class 5. What was the mean number of books read by each child during the first four weeks of the readathon?

11.   If $3(x - 2) = 39$, what is x? Circle the correct option.

    A   34   **C**   15   **E**   13.6

    B   13   **D**   11

12.   Steven makes up a sequence. Each term in Steven's sequence is odd.
      Circle the expression that could give the nth term of Steven's sequence.

    A $2n$ **C** $2n + 1$ **E** n^2

    B $3n$ **D** $2n + 2$

/ 12

You have **10 minutes** to do this test. Work as quickly and accurately as you can.

1. £180 is shared out equally between some brothers. Each brother gets £30.
    How many brothers are there?

2. The net below is folded into a cube.

    The cube is placed so that the grey face, [ ], is at the top.
    Which face is at the bottom? Circle the correct answer.

    A   B ✛   C ◆   D ■   E ✦

3. Karen counts back in threes from 17. What is the first number less than zero
    that she will count? Circle the correct option.

    A   −1   C   −3   E   −5
    B   −2   D   −4

4. Ahmed is making fizzy apple juice. He pours 1.75 litres of apple juice into
    a jug and adds 500 ml of lemonade. He then drinks 150 ml of the mixture.
    How many litres are left in the jug? Circle the correct answer.

    A   1.9 litres   C   2.1 litres   E   1.6 litres
    B   6.6 litres   D   5.25 litres

The children in a primary school were asked how many of their baby teeth they'd lost. The results are shown in the table.

Number of teeth lost	Number of children
0	30
1 - 3	25
4 - 6	35
7 - 9	20
10 - 12	21
more than 12	19

5. How many children had lost more than six teeth?

6. What fraction of the children hadn't lost any teeth?
   Circle the correct answer.

   A $\frac{1}{4}$ **B** $\frac{1}{5}$ **C** $\frac{3}{5}$ **D** $\frac{3}{4}$ **E** $\frac{1}{6}$

7. To make a certain shade of green, you mix one part blue paint with five parts yellow paint. Kay wants to have 300 ml of green paint in total. How much blue paint should she use?

   ml

8. Pound coins have a mass of 9.5 g each. Sarah puts 100 of them into an empty money box which has a mass of 75 g. What is the total mass of her money box, including coins, now? Give your answer in kilograms.

   kg

9. Hannah runs for 90 seconds, then walks for two minutes. She repeats this six times, starting at 10:49 am. What time does she finish?

   am

10. The volume of this cuboid is 348 m³.

3 m

5 m

What is the cuboid's length?

 m

11. A triangle on a coordinate grid is translated to a new position as shown.

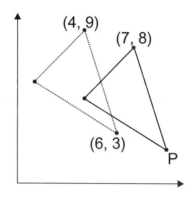

(4, 9)

(7, 8)

(6, 3)

P

What are the coordinates of point P? Circle the correct answer.

A   (2, 9)

B   (3, 2)

C   (9, 2)

D   (8, 2)

E   (9, 4)

12. A gardener uses the formula $C = 50 + 0.9m$ to work out C, the cost in pounds for cutting a hedge, where m is the length of the hedge in metres.
What will be the cost of having a 20 metre hedge cut?

£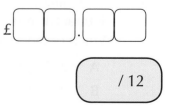

/ 12

You have **10 minutes** to do this test. Work as quickly and accurately as you can.

1. The timetable below shows the times that a bus stops in six different towns.
    The bus always runs exactly on time.

Broom	Easton	Yew Bridge	Richby	Clayton	Fryton
0852	0927	0957	1014	1039	1104

How long, in minutes, does it take for the bus to get from Easton to Fryton?

 minutes

2. Find the difference between the smallest and largest numbers listed below.

88.10,   87.43,   87.62,   88.04

3. Look at the diagram below.

Circle the best estimate for the size of angle *x* from the options below.

A 100°   **B** 200°   **C** 160°   **D** 260°   **E** 181°

4. Clive makes a sequence using the following rule:
    'Subtract 1 from the previous number, then multiply the result by 4'.
    Which of the following could be Clive's sequence? Circle the correct option.

A   2, 7, 27...   **C**   3, 12, 48...   **E**   3, 8, 32...

B   3, 2, 1...   **D**   2, 4, 12...

A TV presenter wishes a happy birthday to some children.
The ages of the children who are wished a happy birthday are 5, 6, 8, 2, 4 and 5.

5.   What is the mean age of these children? Circle the correct answer.

    A 4.5   **B** 5   **C** 5.5   **D** 6   **E** 6.5

6.   Two of these children are boys. The mean age of the girls is 6.
How old are the boys?

 and

7.   Jo needs to pack away 1204 Christmas tree baubles. She can fit nine in each box.
How many boxes will she need?

8.   Ranjit makes a pie chart to show the number of cars of each colour in a car park.

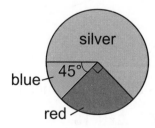

There were 23 blue cars. How many silver cars were there?

9. | $138 \times 44 = 6072$ |

Circle the incorrect calculation below.

    A $138 \times 22 = 6072 \div 2$

    B $138 \times 88 = 6072 \times 2$

    C $138 \times 11 = 6072 \div 4$

    D $138 \times 4.4 = 6072 \div 100$

    E $138 \times 440 = 6072 \times 10$

10. Ryan is buying some trainers. They usually cost £48 but there is 35% off the price in a sale. Ryan also has a student card that gets him 10% off the sale price. How much will Ryan pay?

£

11. Darcey is thinking of a number. She says, "The number is a prime number between 30 and 50. It is one more than a multiple of 7." What number is she thinking of?

12. The shape below is a kite.

Circle the expression that gives the kite's perimeter.

    A $x + 9$ C $2x + 18$ E $2x + 12$

    B $9x + 9$ D $9x$

/ 12

Now for a break from 10-minute tests. Try out your skills on these puzzles.

Cake Cutting

Six people at a party share a cake.
They each have a different sized piece.
Use the clues to work out who has
which slice of cake.

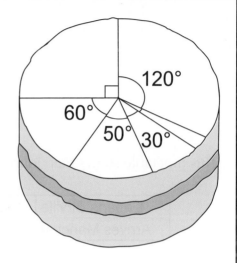

Clare and Dillon together ate $^1/_3$ of the cake.
Adam and Gosia together ate $^1/_2$ the cake.
Clare and Fred together ate $^1/_3$ of the amount
that Adam did. Eve ate the rest.

Symbol Sums

In the addition and multiplication below, most of the digits have been
replaced by symbols. A symbol that is used in both calculations represents
the same digit in both. Each symbol represents a different digit.

$$\begin{array}{r} \triangle * \blacksquare \\ + \triangle * \triangle \\ \hline * 5\ 2 \\ 1\ 1 \end{array} \qquad \begin{array}{r} \Downarrow \star \heartsuit \\ \times \quad \blacksquare \\ \hline \Downarrow 5 \Uparrow \obot \\ 7\ 3 \end{array}$$

Work out which digit each symbol represents and write
it in the correct box below.

$\triangle = \square$ $\blacksquare = \square$ $* = \square$ $\star = \square$

$\obot = \square$ $\Uparrow = \square$ $\heartsuit = \square$ $\Downarrow = \square$

You have **10 minutes** to do this test. Work as quickly and accurately as you can.

1. What number will correctly complete the following calculation?

   | _____ × 15 = 30 + 30 + 30 |

This timetable shows train journey times between the towns of Birville and Mancton.

Departs Birville	0931	0957	1031	1057	1131
Arrives Mancton	1059	1125	1159	1225	1259

2. How long is the train journey between the towns?

    minutes

3. Juliana needs to be in Mancton by noon. It takes her $^3/_4$ of an hour to get to Birville station from her house. What is the latest time she could leave her house to get to Mancton on time?

4. Mel is describing a shape. She says, 'It is an irregular quadrilateral. Its diagonals are always lines of symmetry.'
   Circle the shape is Mel describing from the options below.

   A   Square
   B   Rectangle
   C   Rhombus
   D   Parallelogram
   E   Trapezium

5. Kyle spends the following amounts on snacks each day from Monday to Friday:

> £2.00 £1.00 £1.50 £2.25 £1.25

What is the mean amount Kyle spends per day?

£

6. Which of the following numbers is the same as $^{18}/_8$?
    Circle the correct answer.

    A   1.75   **B**   2.2   **C**   2.25   **D**   2.5   **E**   2.8

7. In a bag of nuts and raisins, there are four nuts for every raisin.
    There are 96 nuts in a bag. How many nuts and raisins are there in total?
    Circle the correct option.

    A   24   **B**   100   **C**   120   **D**   200   **E**   216

8. Asif wants to make a cardboard net of the cuboid shown below.

What will the area of the net be?

☐☐ cm²

Jamie sells jam in four different flavours at a market stall.
The chart below shows the proportions of each flavour that he sells in one day.

9. Why is the chart misleading? Circle the correct option.

    A   It doesn't show all of the flavours of jam Jamie sold.

    B   It doesn't show how many jars of each jam were sold.

    C   The scale doesn't increase evenly.

    D   The jar narrows at the top, so the top section looks smaller than it should.

    E   The sections are not coloured to match the different jams.

10. Jamie sells 90 jars of jam in total that day. How many of these were raspberry?
Circle the correct answer.

    A   36   **B**   40   **C**   45   **D**   81   **E**   90

A phone company charges C pence to make an international phone call
lasting m minutes, where $C = 25 + 6m$.

11. Marco spends half an hour on an international call.
How much does it cost?

    £ ☐☐.☐☐

12. Carla spends 85p on an international call that ends at 20:02.
What time did her call start?

    ☐☐:☐☐

/ 12

You have **10 minutes** to do this test. Work as quickly and accurately as you can.

1. Eve thinks of a number between 60 and 80 which is a multiple of both 4 and 9.
    What is the number?

Santino has made 4.5 litres of fruit punch.

2. 1 litre is approximately 1.8 pints.
    Which of these is the best approximation of the number of
    pints of punch Santino has made? Circle the correct option.

    A 2   **B** 2$\frac{1}{2}$ **C** 5   **D** 8   **E** 20

3. Santino serves the punch in 150 ml cups.
    How many cups can he fill?

4. The third, fourth and fifth terms of a sequence are: –4, –7 and –10.
    What was the first term of the sequence?

5. Which of the following is not equal to the others? Circle the correct option.

    A $\frac{3}{4}$ of 36
    B 10% of 270
    C $\frac{1}{2}$ of 54
    D 0.270 × 100
    E $\frac{2}{7}$ of 10

6. Look at the equation below.

$$12345 \div \boxed{} = 12.345 \times \boxed{}$$

Circle the pair of numbers which cannot be written in the boxes in the order given.

A   1000 and 1   **C**   100 and 100   **E**   1 and 1000

B   100 and 10   **D**   10 and 100

7. The population of a town is thirty-two thousand five hundred, rounded to the nearest hundred. Circle the largest number the population could be.

A   32 500   **B**   32 450   **C**   32 550   **D**   32 549   **E**   31 549

8. The graph below can be used to convert between temperatures measured in Fahrenheit (°F) and temperatures measured in Celsius (°C).

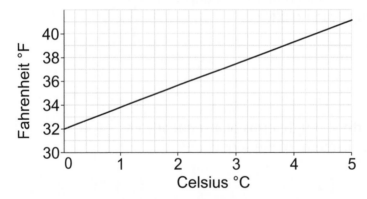

Use the graph to find the difference in temperature between 36 °F and 40 °F, in degrees Celsius, to one decimal place.

9. A circle has a diameter of 0.01 m. What is its radius? Circle the correct answer.

A   1 cm   **C**   5 cm   **E**   5 mm

B   2 cm   **D**   2 mm

10. A pie shop sells vegetable pies and meat pies. The prices are shown below.

vegetable £1.50	meat £3.00

One day 50 pies are sold in total.
20 of these are vegetable pies and the rest are meat pies.
The shopkeeper records how much money is made from selling each type of pie.
He wants to show his results on a pie chart. What angle should he use for the section representing the money made from selling vegetable pies?

 °

11. A net of a cube is drawn on a rectangular sheet of paper, as shown.

The whole sheet of paper has an area of 48 cm².
What will be the volume of the cube made from the net?

 cm³

12. Look at the triangle shown on the right.
Circle the equation which is correct
for this triangle.

A $12y + 20° = 180°$

B $12y = 360°$

C $6y = 90°$

D $12y = 200°$

E $6y - 10° = 90°$

/ 12

🕙 10

You have **10 minutes** to do this test. Work as quickly and accurately as you can.

1.   How many rectangular faces does a triangular prism have?

Customers in a pet shop were asked whether they owned a cat or a dog.
The partly filled table shows the results.

	cat	no cat	**total**
dog	26		
no dog			42
total	57		**100**

2.   How many customers didn't own either a cat or a dog?

3.   What percentage of customers owned a dog?

 %

4.   A point with coordinates (–1, –3) is reflected in the *y*-axis.
      Which of the points below has the same coordinates as the reflected point?

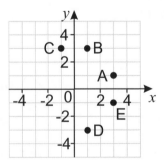

Circle the correct letter.

| **A** | **B** | **C** | **D** | **E** |

5. A piece of string is cut into four pieces. The mean length of the pieces is 10 cm.
Circle the option below which does not give possible lengths of three of the pieces.

    A   10 cm, 10 cm and 10 cm

    B   10 cm, 12 cm and 14 cm

    C   1 cm, 2 cm and 3 cm

    D   7 cm, 11 cm and 23 cm

    E   13 cm, 13 cm and 13 cm

6. Work out $4\frac{1}{2} - 3\frac{4}{5}$.
Give your answer as a decimal.

$$\boxed{}\boxed{}.\boxed{}\boxed{}$$

7. The pictogram on the right shows the number adults () and children ( ) at a sports match.

Both symbols represent the same number of people. There were 1250 more adults than children.

What number does ![symbol] represent in the key?

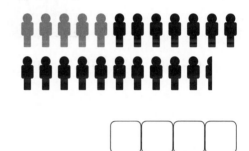

$$\boxed{}\boxed{}\boxed{}\boxed{}$$

8. The shape below is a parallelogram.

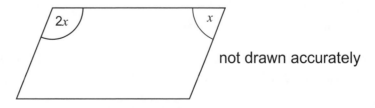

not drawn accurately

What is the size of angle x? Circle the correct answer.

    A   30°   **B**   45°   **C**   60°   **D**   90°   **E**   120°

Adah is making a large rice dish for 30 people.
She is scaling up a recipe that uses 320 g of rice and serves 4 people.

9. How much rice will she need for 30 people?
    Give your answer in kilograms.

     kg

10. What percentage of the rice will be wasted if only 24 people are served?
    Circle the correct answer.

    A   6%   **B**   15%   **C**   20%   **D**   25%   **E**   80%

11. A square with a perimeter of 316 mm is cut in half along its diagonal.
    The two halves are rearranged to form a parallelogram, as shown.

    not drawn accurately

    Find the area of the parallelogram.

     mm^2

12. A sequence is made of rectangles, as shown below.

    Which of these expressions describes the perimeter of the nth shape
    in the sequence? Circle the correct answer.

    A $n \times 3n$ **C** $n + 3n$ **E** $8n$

    B $n + n + 3$ **D** $2(n + 3)$

    / 12

You have **10 minutes** to do this test. Work as quickly and accurately as you can.

1. What is 123 456 rounded to the nearest 100?

2. The diagram below shows points Y and Z.

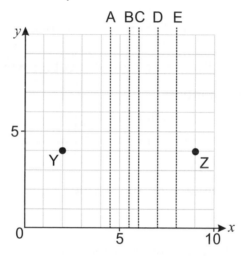

Point Y was reflected in a mirror line to give point Z.
Which mirror line, A, B, C, D or E, was this?

3. The seventh term of a sequence is 64.
Which of the following could not be the start of the sequence?
Circle the option which cannot show the sequence.

    A   1, 2, 4, 8, 16, ...
    B   34, 39, 44, 49, 54, ...
    C   4, 9, 16, 25, 36, ...
    D   100, 94, 88, 82, 76, ...
    E   8, 17, 26, 35, 44, ...

4. There are two prime numbers between 60 and 70.
What is the difference between them?

59

Rose walks along a path through a park.
The graph shows her journey from the start of the path to the end.

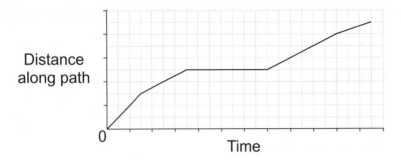

Rose stopped for $3^1/_2$ minutes at a point 125 m along the path.

5. Which of these statements is true? Circle the correct answer.

    A Rose stopped after 7 minutes.

    B Rose walked another 125 m after she stopped.

    C Rose reached the end of the path after 11 minutes.

    D Rose walked 225 m in total.

    E Rose walked for 5 minutes after she stopped.

6. Once at the end of the path, Rose walked back to the start of the path.
    She took the same amount of time to walk back along the path as she
    had taken to reach the end of it. She finished the whole walk at 13:07.
    What time did she start?

    ⬜⬜:⬜⬜

Jay has 24 coins in a jar. $^7/_{12}$ of these are 10p coins, $^1/_4$ are 20p coins
and the rest are 50p coins.

7. What fraction of the coins are 50p coins? Circle the correct answer.

    A $^1/_{24}$ **B** $^1/_{12}$ **C** $^1/_6$ **D** $^1/_3$ **E** $^1/_2$

8. How much money does Jay have in the jar?

    £⬜⬜.⬜⬜

In a rabbit race, Bugs covers 65 cm with every hop.
The race track is 14.3 m long.

9. How many hops does Bugs take to complete the race?
    Circle the correct option.

    A 2   **B** 3   **C** 22   **D** 200   **E** 220

10. A carrot is pulled along the race track to encourage Bugs to hop. It is pulled a
    distance of 0.5 metres every second. How long does it take for the carrot to be
    pulled along the whole track? Round your answer to the nearest second.

     seconds

11. $41 - 3h = 17$.
    What is h?

12. There are three different paths on a cycle trail, each with a different level of
    challenge. The pie chart below shows the number of cyclists who took each path,
    out of a total of 80 cyclists.

    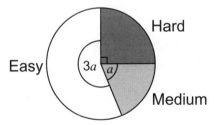

    How many cyclists took the easy path?

    / 12

You have **10 minutes** to do this test. Work as quickly and accurately as you can.

1. Deena had a negative amount of money in her bank account. She then paid in twenty-seven pounds, which made the amount of money in the account positive. Which of the following could be the amounts in Deena's bank account before and after she paid in the money? Circle the correct option.

    A   −£5 and +£32

    B   −£7 and +£21

    C   −£8 and +£19

    D   −£9 and +£19

    E   −£9 and +£17

2. What is the volume of the cuboid shown below?

6 m

4 m

2.5 m

☐☐☐ m³

3. Five friends share $^1/_3$ of a loaf of bread equally.
    What fraction of the whole loaf does each person get? Circle the correct answer.

    A $^5/_3$ **B** $^3/_5$ **C** $^1/_8$ **D** $^1/_9$ **E** $^1/_{15}$

4. The sum of the angles inside a regular octagon is 1080°.
    What is the size of each angle?

    ☐☐☐ °

Pupils in Year 6 were asked how many pets they owned.
The results are shown in the bar chart.

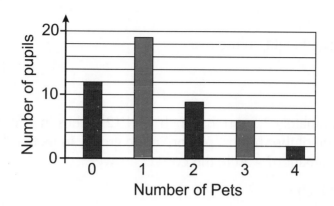

5.   What fraction of the pupils owned at least three pets? Circle the correct answer.

   A $^1/_{24}$ **B** $^1/_6$ **C** $^1/_8$ **D** $^1/_3$ **E** $^5/_6$

6.   How many pets are owned in total by the pupils in Year 6?

A giant bar of chocolate is 8 squares wide by 20 squares long, and costs £3.80.

7.   The bar is shared out between 9 people so each has the same number of squares.
     How many squares are left over?

8.   The bar is reduced in price by 15%. What is the reduced price?

     £ ☐ . ☐ ☐

Four people record their heights. These are given below:

1.55 m   125 cm   1.7 m   162 cm

9.   What is their mean height, in metres?

 m

10. There are approximately 2.5 cm in 1 inch, and 12 inches in 1 foot.
     What is the height of the shortest person in the group, in feet and inches,
     using this approximation? Circle the correct answer.

     A   3 feet 10 inches
     B   4 feet 2 inches
     C   5 feet
     D   5 feet 2 inches
     E   5 feet 10 inches

The square and rectangle below have the same area.

a

b

$b + 5$

11. Circle the expression below which does not represent this area.

     A $a \times a$ **C** a^2 **E** $2b + 5$
     B $b(b + 5)$ **D** $b(5 + b)$

12. b is a whole number.
     If $a = 6$ cm, what is b?

 cm

/ 12

Now for a break from 10-minute tests. Try out your skills on these puzzles.

In a Pickle

Padma wants to make lime pickle, using up what she has in her cupboard.
For every 8 limes, she needs 125 g sugar, 3 garlic cloves and approximately
8 cm³ of ginger. She has the following amounts of each of these in her cupboard:

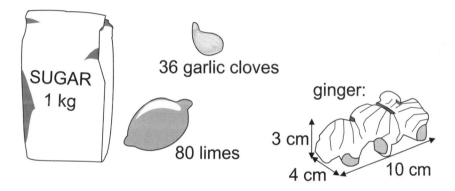

SUGAR 1 kg

36 garlic cloves

80 limes

ginger:
3 cm
4 cm
10 cm

Padma makes as much pickle as possible with what she has in the cupboard.
How much of each ingredient above will she have left over?

Riddle Me This

What's my name?

My first is one hundred to a Roman,
and my last is a line
perpendicular to *x* on a grid.

My third looks like a shape with a circumference,
and my second the symbol for half its diameter.

My fourth is the first of an angle less than 90°,
and my fifth is the first of a quadrilateral you can fly.

10

You have **10 minutes** to do this test. Work as quickly and accurately as you can.

1.   David makes a sequence of numbers starting with 380. He subtracts 75 each time.

380   305   230   155...

What is the next number in the sequence?

Jackson goes to the park for 2 hours.

2.   Jackson spends 15% of his time playing on the swings.
How many minutes does Jackson play on the swings for?

minutes

3.   Jackson leaves the park at 15:48.
The clock shows the time that he arrives back at his house that afternoon.

How many minutes does it take Jackson to get home?

minutes

4.   Leina eats $^1/_4$ of a cake. Jonathan eats $^2/_5$ of the same cake.
What fraction of the cake have they eaten in total? Circle the correct option.

   A $^3/_9$ **B** $^6/_9$ **C** $^2/_{20}$ **D** $^7/_{20}$ **E** $^{13}/_{20}$

5. Kelly chooses two of the cards shown below.

$$5 \quad 7 \quad 9 \quad 11$$

She multiplies the numbers on her two cards together and then subtracts 7.
She rounds the result to the nearest 10. Her answer is 50.
Which two cards did Kelly choose? Circle the correct option.

A   5 and 9   **C**   7 and 9   **E**   9 and 11

B   5 and 11   **D**   7 and 11

Jimmy asked the pupils at his school if they
like football, tennis and swimming.
He recorded the number of people who
like each sport in a Venn diagram.

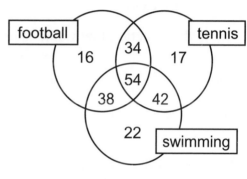

6. How many of the pupils like tennis?

7. How many of the pupils don't like football?

8. Benji is at an ice cream parlour. The menu is shown below.

Menu	
2 scoops of ice cream	£2.40
Additional scoops	£0.90 each
Toppings (sprinkles, sauce, marshmallows)	£0.55 each

Benji has £7.40 to spend.
He buys 4 scoops of ice cream with sprinkles and marshmallows.
How much money does Benji have left?

£

9. Skyla and Paloma take part in a race.
    Skyla runs at a constant speed and covers a distance of 10 km every hour.
    Paloma runs at a constant speed and covers a distance of 12 km every hour.
    How much further than Skyla has Paloma run after 15 minutes?

     km

10. Callie is facing North (N). She makes the following turns.

    • 135° anti-clockwise.
    • 45° clockwise.

    Circle the direction that Callie is now facing.

    A NE   **C** W   **E** S
    B NW   **D** SE

11. Claire has 5 different right-angled triangles.
    Which of her triangles is the tallest? Circle the correct option.

    A A triangle with a base of 6 cm and an area of 21 cm².
    B A triangle with a base of 5 cm and an area of 20 cm².
    C A triangle with a base of 3 cm and an area of 15 cm².
    D A triangle with a base of 8 cm and an area of 8 cm².
    E A triangle with a base of 4 cm and an area of 12 cm².

12. This diagram shows the angles of
    each sector in a circle.
    What is the value of a?

/ 12

You have **10 minutes** to do this test. Work as quickly and accurately as you can.

1. Sharon buys five items in a shop. Which of the following shows the prices in order of size, starting from the smallest? Circle the correct option.

    A 45p £4.50 £4.05 £0.54 £5.40

    B 45p £0.54 £4.05 £4.50 £5.40

    C £0.54 45p £4.05 £4.50 £5.40

    D 45p £0.54 £4.05 £5.40 £4.50

    E £0.54 45p £5.40 £4.05 £4.50

2. Brenda has a piece of ribbon that is 1 m long. She cuts off 4 cm of ribbon. She then cuts the remaining piece of ribbon into 8 equal lengths.
   How long is each of these 8 equal lengths?

   ☐☐ cm

3. Kian is sorting some numbers into a table.

	Even	Odd
Multiple of 9		
Multiple of 7		

   Circle the group of numbers below that would be sorted into the grey box.

   A 21, 42, 49   **C** 21, 35, 77   **E** 18, 45, 81

   B 27, 45, 81   **D** 14, 42, 54

4. Circle the fraction below that is bigger than $^3/_5$.

   A $^{13}/_{20}$ **C** $^6/_{10}$ **E** $^8/_{15}$

   B $^1/_6$ **D** $^3/_6$

5. Tamwar is measuring 2 of his toy cars.

How much bigger is Car A than Car B? Give your answer in mm.

 mm

6. Hazel draws the shape to the right.
    She reflects the shape in Line Y.

    Which of the following shows her new shape?
    Circle the correct option.

7. Tahlia records the eye colour of 72 pupils in Year 6.
    6 pupils have hazel eyes.
    Circle the number of pupils that have green eyes.

    A 9
    B 12
    C 15
    D 18
    E 21

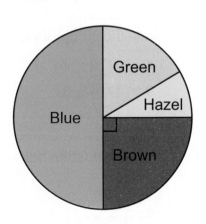

8. Chernice has a jar containing 500 g of jelly beans. 23% of the jelly beans are red. 47% of the jelly beans are blue. The rest of the jelly beans are green.
How much do the green jelly beans weigh?

⬚⬚⬚ g

Juanita buys m packs of stickers. Sanjit buys 4 more packs of stickers than Juanita.

9. Circle the expression which shows how many packs of stickers they bought in total.

    A $m + 4$ **B** $5m$ **C** $2m + 4$ **D** $2(m + 4)$ **E** $4m + 2$

10. They bought 16 packs of stickers in total.
How many packs of stickers did Sanjit buy?

⬚⬚

A group of five children are selling homemade lemonade.
The pictogram shows how many cups of lemonade each child has sold.

Jenson	🍋 🍋 🍋 ◁
Carlton	🍋 🍋 🍋 🍋 🍋 🍋 ◁
Bella	🍋 🍋 🍋
Casey	🍋 🍋 🍋 🍋 ◁

Key: 🍋 = 4 cups

11. Each cup sold contains 220 ml of lemonade.
How many more litres has Carlton sold than Casey?

⬚.⬚⬚ litres

12. The ingredients for the lemonade cost £15.90.
The children sell each cup of lemonade for £1.20.
How much profit have the children made in total?

£⬚⬚.⬚⬚

/ 12

You have **10 minutes** to do this test. Work as quickly and accurately as you can.

1. | 100 × _____ = 3640 |

    What is the missing value? Circle the correct option.

    A   364   **B**   36.4   **C**   3.64   **D**   364000   **E**   36400

2. The contents page of a book is shown below. It shows what page each chapter in the book starts on. The book is 227 pages long.
    Which is the longest chapter? Circle the correct option.

    A   Chapter 1
    B   Chapter 2
    C   Chapter 3
    D   Chapter 4
    E   Chapter 5

Contents
Chapter 1............1
Chapter 2..........31
Chapter 3..........76
Chapter 4........134
Chapter 5........185

Some of the angles in the diagram below have been labelled.

3. Which angles are acute?
    Circle the correct option.

    A   Angle *d*, Angle *f* and Angle *g*
    B   Angle *e*, Angle *f* and Angle *h*
    C   Angle *d* and Angle *g*
    D   Angle *d* and Angle *f*
    E   Angle *f*, Angle *g* and Angle *h*

4. Angle *g* is 46°. What is the size of Angle *h*?

     °

5. John and Robyn walk together across the playground.
    For every 2 steps that John takes, Robyn takes 3 steps.
    If John takes 54 steps, how many steps does Robyn take?

6. A pack of 6 beef burgers costs £4.20.
A pack of 5 lamb burgers costs £3.00.
How much more does one beef burger cost than one lamb burger?

£ .

The timeline below shows what time Giovanna eats her meals each day.

7. Giovanna goes to the park 1 hour and 20 minutes before she has lunch.
What time does she go to the park?

 am

8. Giovanna takes 25 minutes to eat her lunch. She then watches a film for
1 hour and 30 minutes and then does some painting for 1 hour and 55 minutes.
When she finishes painting, how long does she have to wait until dinner time?

hour(s) mins

9. The diagram below shows the coordinates of each corner of a rectangle.

Which of the following points
will be inside the rectangle?
Circle the correct option.

A (−65, −32)

B (−17, 36)

C (23, −23)

D (18, 30)

E (−41, 6)

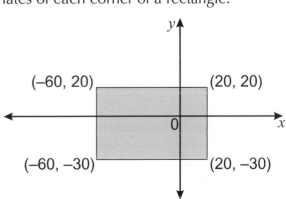

10. Use estimation to work out the number that is halfway between 342.6 and 1393.8. Circle the correct option.

    A   736.2

    B   783.7

    C   868.2

    D   899.2

    E   922.5

The bar chart shows the number of points competitors scored in a sports competition.

11. The mean number of points scored by each competitor was 63.3. What was the total of all the points scored by the competitors?

12. What might have been the number of points scored by the person who came in 15th place? Circle the correct option.

    A   59

    B   85

    C   76

    D   69

    E   42

/ 12

You have **10 minutes** to do this test. Work as quickly and accurately as you can.

1. How many numbers between 10 and 20 are factors of 36?

2. Which of the following pairs of numbers have a difference of 0.37?
   Circle the correct option.

   A   1.24 and 1.66   **C**   1.0 and 4.7   **E**   9.22 and 9.58

   B   0.31 and 0.38   **D**   4.81 and 5.18

Eliza is making cornflake cakes.
The ingredients for making 18 cornflake cakes are shown below.

> Ingredients
>
> *To make 18 cakes.*
>
> 75 g butter
> 150 g chocolate
> 4.5 tbsp golden syrup
> 150 g cornflakes

Eliza only has 50 g of butter.

3. How many grams of chocolate will she need to use?

4. How many cakes can Eliza make?

5. Zoe is describing a type of quadrilateral.
   It has a pair of equal parallel sides which are a different length to another pair of equal parallel sides.
   Half of its angles are acute and the other half are obtuse.

   What shape is Zoe describing? Circle the correct option.

   A parallelogram   **C** square   **E** trapezium
   B rectangle   **D** rhombus

6. What is $2^3 + 3^2 + 3^3 + 5^2$?

7. Callum is making a dice from a net. Opposite sides of a dice add up to 7.
   Which net must he use? Circle the correct option.

            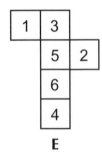

   A   **B**   **C**   **D**   **E**

8. The kite on the right is enlarged by a scale factor of 2.5.
   What is the perimeter of the enlarged kite?
   Circle the correct answer.

   A   5.2 cm
   B   13 cm
   C   16.25 cm
   D   32.5 cm
   E   39 cm

line of symmetry

2.6 cm

3.9 cm

not drawn accurately

A cinema shows 'A Dog's Life' once a day for a week.
The table below shows the number of tickets sold on each weekday.

Ticket	Monday	Tuesday	Wednesday	Thursday	Friday
Adult	19	28	21	13	33
Child	47	54	30	16	37
Family (2 adults and 2 children)	7	26	9	3	11

9.   All the adults who had a ticket saw the film.
     How many more adults saw the film on Friday than saw it on Monday?

10. Adult tickets are £10, child tickets are £6 and family tickets are £25.
     How much money did the cinema make from 'A Dog's Life' tickets on Thursday?

11. The pie chart shows sales of the different types of cinema tickets for one day.

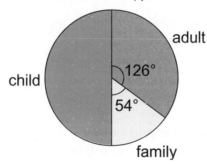

     Which day does the pie chart show? Circle the correct option.

     A   Monday   **C**   Wednesday   **E**   Friday
     B   Tuesday   **D**   Thursday

12. Marley writes an expression.
     When $x = 7$ and $y = 3$, the value of the expression is 84.
     Circle Marley's expression from the options below.

     A $6x + 12y$ **C** $4xy$ **E** $5xy - 10$
     B $7x + y^2 + 15$ **D** $x^2 + 4y - xy$

/ 12

77

You have **10 minutes** to do this test. Work as quickly and accurately as you can.

Kim has 560 beads for making necklaces.

1. Kim divides the beads into 7 equal piles. How many beads are in each pile?

2. Kim puts 50 beads on some string. Each bead is 13 mm long.
    What is the total length of beads?

 mm

3. Angelee makes the shape on the right from 9 cubes.
    She paints spots on the side faces of the shape
    and leaves the top and bottom faces blank.
    She then separates the shape back into 9 cubes.

    How many cubes have exactly two spotted faces?

4. A shape has been draw onto the grid below.
    One of the corners of the shape has been labelled with a cross.
    The shape is reflected in the *y*-axis.
    What are the new coordinates of the labelled corner?

The pupils at Pobbleton Primary School earn stars for good behaviour in a lesson.
The stars earned by 36 girls and 28 boys in a day are shown on the pie charts below.

Girls

Boys

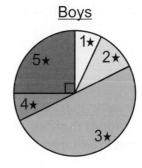

5. Which of the following statements is true? Circle the correct option.

    A   The same number of boys and girls got 5 stars.

    B   Two more girls than boys got 5 stars.

    C   70% of the girls got fewer than 5 stars.

    D   Half of the children got 5 stars.

    E   Eighteen pupils got 5 stars.

6. How many more boys than girls earned exactly 3 stars?

7. A design is made up of regular octagons and squares.
    Each octagon has a perimeter of 24 cm.
    What is the perimeter of the shaded region in the design?
    Circle the correct option.

    A   39 cm   C   48 cm   E   72 cm

    B   45 cm   D   63 cm

    not drawn
    accurately

8. Connie is thinking of two prime numbers between 1 and 20.
    The difference between them is 10.
    She adds the two numbers together. Her answer is 24.
    What two numbers is Connie thinking of?

     and

79

Dulcie aims to drink at least 2 litres of water every day.

9. So far today, Dulcie has drunk 460 ml of water.
    What percentage of her target water volume has Dulcie drunk?

    [   ][   ] %

10. Dulcie uses the same glass all day. The glass holds 290 ml of water.
    What is the minimum number of glasses that she needs to drink throughout the
    whole day to meet her target? Circle the correct option.

    A   5   **C**   8   **E**   6
    B   7   **D**   10

11. Martha is weighing some of her toys.

    The teddy and the car weigh the same as the jack-in-the-box.
    The toys weigh 894 g in total. The car weighs 182 g.
    How many kilograms does the teddy weigh?

    [   ].[   ][   ][   ] kg

12. Manoj thinks of a number.
    He puts the number into the formula $2(x^2 - 14)$ in place of x. His answer is 44.
    What number is Manoj thinking of? Circle the correct option.

    A   4   **C**   9   **E**   18
    B   6   **D**   10

    / 12

Now for a break from 10-minute tests. Try out your skills on this puzzle.

Percy's Picture Puzzle

Percy needs some help putting a picture of his pet back together.

Each piece of the puzzle contains a maths problem and part of the picture. Help Percy put the picture back together by finding the box in the grid which contains the correct answer and drawing in the correct part of the picture.

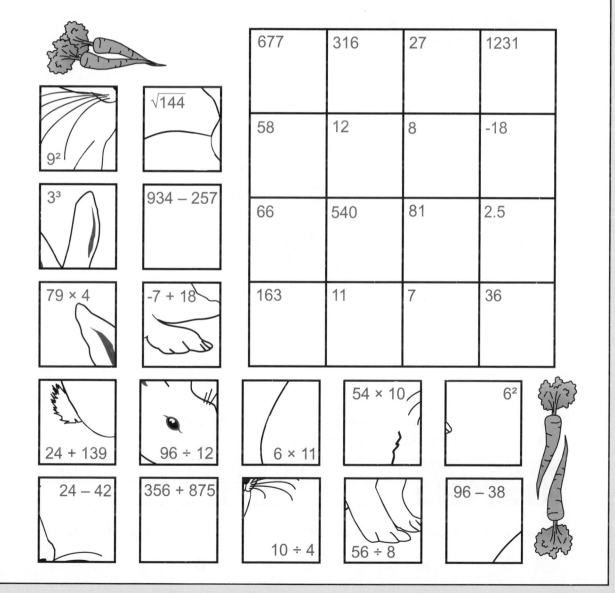

Test 26

You have **10 minutes** to do this test. Work as quickly and accurately as you can.

1. Taz receives a cheque for seven hundred and four thousand, three hundred and five pounds and eight pence.
   Write this amount in figures.

   £ ⬚⬚⬚⬚⬚⬚ . ⬚⬚

2. The first five terms in a sequence are: 2, 5, 8, 11 and 14.
   What is the 10th term?

   ⬚⬚⬚

3. Louis asks the people coming to his party if they are vegetarians, vegans or neither. He makes a pie chart to show the results.

   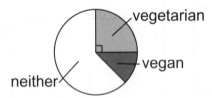

   If there are 6 vegetarians coming to the party, how many guests are coming in total?

   ⬚⬚⬚

4. Owen makes the following table to show how many books of each different type he has on his bookshelf.

Type of Book	Poetry	Fantasy	Sci-Fi	History	Other
Number of Books	3	7	5	2	1

   What fraction of Owen's books are fantasy or sci-fi? Circle the correct answer.

   A $^1/_{18}$ **B** $^1/_{12}$ **C** $^1/_3$ **D** $^1/_2$ **E** $^2/_3$

5. A square has an area of 9 cm². What is its perimeter?
   Circle the correct option.

   A 3 cm   **C** 2.25 cm   **E** 36 cm

   B 12 cm   **D** 30 cm

6. An equilateral triangle is shown below.

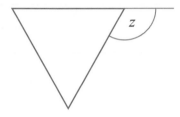

   What is the size of angle *z*? Circle the correct option.

   A 30°   **C** 120°   **E** Impossible to tell

   B 60°   **D** 300°

A shape is made on a grid from a
rectangle and 4 triangles, as shown.

7. How many lines of symmetry does the shape have?

8. Circle the statement below which is false.

   A The ratio of the total area of the triangles to the area of the rectangle is 2 : 3.

   B The rectangle takes up 60% of the total area of the shape.

   C The area of one triangle is $^1/_6$ of the area of the rectangle.

   D The area of the rectangle is the same as the total area of 3 triangles.

   E The area of one triangle is 10% of the total area of the shape.

                                       Test 26

9. An oven has a width of 76 cm, rounded to the nearest whole centimetre.
It is fitted into a space with a width of 77.5 cm, rounded to one decimal place.
Circle the option which correctly gives the smallest possible oven width and the smallest possible space width.

	Smallest possible oven width	Smallest possible space width
A	75.5 cm	77.55 cm
B	75.49 cm	77.49 cm
C	75.5 cm	77.45 cm
D	76.5 cm	77.55 cm
E	75.49 cm	77.45 cm

A group of seven friends make and sell knitted scarves at a market stall.
Each scarf is made from one and a half balls of wool. Each ball of wool costs £2.60.

10. The group sells 30 scarves for a total of £189.
How much profit do they make in total by selling 30 scarves?

£ ☐☐ . ☐☐

11. At closing time one day, the friends are left with £150 to split equally amongst themselves. How much does each friend get, rounded down to the nearest penny?
Circle the correct answer.

A   £20.00   B   £20.43   C   £21.00   D   £21.40   E   £21.42

12. $n < 5 + 4 \times 3$

n is a square number.
What is the largest number that n could be?

☐☐

/ 12

⏱ 10

You have **10 minutes** to do this test. Work as quickly and accurately as you can.

1. The diagram below shows the top view of a weather vane, pointing due east (E).

The wind blows the arrow 270° anticlockwise.
Which direction (N, E, S or W) is it now pointing to?

2. Mike's cousins have a mean age of 8, and a total age of 40.
How many cousins does Mike have?

3. Kaitlyn buys a bottle of a fizzy drink, shown on the right.
The label on the bottle is torn so it does
not give the units for the volume in the bottle.
What are the units most likely to be?
Circle the correct option.

    A grams   **C** millilitres   **E** litres
    B kilograms   **D** millimetres

4. In her purse, Dora has twelve 20 pence pieces and eight 10 pence pieces.
She gives her nephew $^1/_3$ of the 20 pence pieces and $^1/_4$ of the 10 pence pieces.
How much money has Dora given her nephew?

£ ⬜ . ⬜⬜

5. How many factors of 60 are prime numbers?

6. Lola has $3^3/_4$ packs of chocolate buttons.
   She eats $^1/_5$ of a pack of chocolate buttons.
   How many packs of buttons does she have left?
   Circle the correct option.

   A $2^3/_4$
   B $2^4/_5$
   C $3^2/_4$
   D $3^2/_{20}$
   E $3^{11}/_{20}$

The pictogram below shows the number of different types of tree in a wood.

Key: = 25 trees

7. How many more ash trees are there than elm trees?

8. What fraction of the trees are fir trees?
   Circle the correct answer.

   A $^3/_5$
   B $^2/_5$
   C $^1/_4$
   D $^1/_5$
   E $^1/_{10}$

9. A regular shape has x sides. One side measures 5 cm.
Circle the expression below which gives the perimeter of the shape.

A $(x + 5)$ cm   **C** $(x \div 5)$ cm   **E** $5x$ cm

B $(x - 5)$ cm   **D** $(5 \div x)$ cm

A number of identical books are to be stacked upright inside boxes, as shown below.

10. What is the maximum number of books that can be placed in one box?

11. There are 1200 books in total. How many books will be left over
if as many boxes as possible are completely filled with books?

12. The nth term in a sequence is $\frac{1}{2}(n + 1)$.
Which term in the sequence has the value 5?
Circle the correct answer.

A 3rd **B** 5th **C** 8th **D** 9th **E** 10th

/ 12

You have **10 minutes** to do this test. Work as quickly and accurately as you can.

1. An office has 7 boxes of 200 paperclips.
   How many paperclips are there in total?

Noah wants to save up £50 to buy his mum a new handbag for her birthday.

2. So far Noah has saved £16.35. How much more money does he need to save?

3. When Noah goes to buy the bag, it is on sale with 25% off.
   By how much is the bag's price reduced in the sale?

4. Each of the shapes below is a regular shape with a side length of 2 cm.
   What is the mean perimeter of the four shapes?

   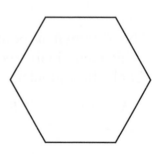

cm

5. The bar chart below, showing the breakfast choices of hotel guests,
    is missing its frequency scale.

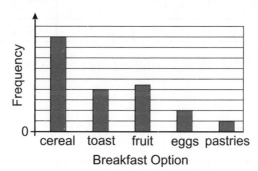

    Which of the following could be the frequencies of the five options?
    Circle the correct list.

    A 9, 4, 5, 2 and 1   **C** 18, 12, 9, 6 and 3   **E** 45, 20, 25, 10 and 5

    B 18, 8, 9, 4 and 1   **D** 36, 16, 18, 8 and 4

6. The diagram below shows a parallelogram and a rectangle.
    They lie next to each other on a straight line.
    What is the size of angle *a*?

7. At a cafe, Amy pays £4.50 for one coffee and one cake,
    and Belle pays £6.25 for two coffees and one cake.
    How much will Kate pay for two cakes?

    £ ☐ . ☐ ☐

8. Abdul has one third of a full melon. He gives one quarter of his melon to Kendra.
    What fraction of a full melon does Kendra have?
    Circle the correct option.

    A $\frac{1}{12}$ **C** $\frac{1}{7}$ **E** $\frac{1}{5}$

    B $\frac{1}{9}$ **D** $\frac{1}{6}$

9. The table shows the finishing times, in seconds, of five swimmers in a race.

Swimmer	Jay	Kim	Li	Mei	Noa
Time (s)	31.26	29.98	30.04	32.01	30.76

How much faster was the winner than the person in second place?

 s

Four of the lettered points on the grid below form the vertices of a parallelogram.

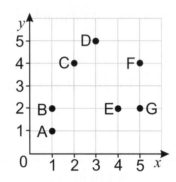

10. Which four letters are the vertices of the parallelogram?
    Circle the correct combination.

    A   A, B, C and D   **C**   C, D, E and F   **E**   C, D, F and G
    B   B, C, F and G   **D**   B, C, E and F

11. Each square on the grid has a width of 0.5 cm.
    Find the area of the parallelogram in cm².

 cm²

12. Ollie walks at a rate of w miles per hour.
    He wants to walk to the bakery, $^3/_4 w$ miles away from his house.
    How many minutes will it take Ollie to walk to the bakery and back home again?

 mins

/ 12

You have **10 minutes** to do this test. Work as quickly and accurately as you can.

1. Kim shares a full packet of biscuits equally between herself, Michael and Sally.
    The full packet weighed 360 g. How many grams of biscuits does Sally get?

 g

Melanie draws three identical stars. She shades a portion of each star blue.

not drawn
accurately

2. What percentage of the three stars' combined area has been shaded blue?

 %

3. The sum of the perimeters of the three stars is 240 cm.
    How long is one side of one star?

☐☐ cm

4. | 1 690 834 ÷ 358 = 4723 |

    What is 1 690 834 ÷ 3.58? Circle the correct option.

    A   4 723 000

    B   472 300

    C   47 230

    D   4723

    E   472.3

91

5.   The rectangle below is made from two triangles.
     The area of each triangle is 14 cm². What is the width of the rectangle?

4 cm

 cm

6.   There are 8 bits in a byte, and 1024 bytes in a kilobyte.
     How many bits are in a kilobyte?

A Year 6 class were asked to vote on whether they wanted to play games on the
last day of term. The results are shown in the pie chart below.

7.   What percentage of the class said "No"? Circle the correct answer.

     A   30%   **B**   35%   **C**   40%   **D**   45%   **E**   72%

8.   12 people said "No". How many more said "Yes"?

9. Alice has £72.00. Elizabeth has £22.50.
Ella has less than $^2/_3$ of the amount that Alice has.
She also has more than double the amount that Elizabeth has.
Circle the amount of money that Ella could have.

   A   £35.20   **C**   £46.50   **E**   £55.30

   B   £44.90   **D**   £49.70

10. Samantha makes a hexagonal prism from the net shown on the right.
Circle the corner which joins to corner M.

   A   Corner V

   B   Corner W

   C   Corner X

   D   Corner Y

   E   Corner Z

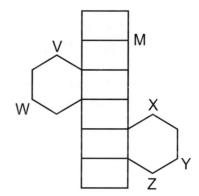

11. 49 000 passes were sold for a festival that takes place over a weekend.
65% of the passes sold were 1-day passes.
35% of the passes sold were 2-day passes.
How many 2-day passes were sold?

12. A mixing bowl has a mass of 90 g. Flour is added to the bowl by the spoonful, with each spoonful having a mass of 10 g. What is the combined mass, in grams, of the bowl and f spoonfuls of flour? Circle the correct expression.

   A $100f$

   B $10f + 90$

   C $10f - 90$

   D $90 + 10 + f$

   E $90f + 10$

/ 12

Test 29

You have **10 minutes** to do this test. Work as quickly and accurately as you can.

1.   What is 10 more than –8?

Lenka has some bunches of grapes and a pack of six apples.
Together the apples and grapes weigh 1.8 kg. The pack of apples weighs 700 g.

2.   What do the grapes weigh?
      Give your answer in kilograms.

 kg

3.   Lenka eats one apple with a mass of 105 g.
      What is the mean mass of the apples that are left?

 g

4.   A shop sells a 2 litre container of milk for 97p. Tim buys 14 litres of milk.
      How much does this cost him?

£

5.   The diagram below shows a square joined to one side of a regular pentagon.

      The pentagon has a perimeter of 35 cm. What is the area of the square?

 cm²

For one week each year in the school holidays, Nora runs a craft workshop for children. The bar chart below shows the number of children who came to the workshop each day of the week this year and last year.

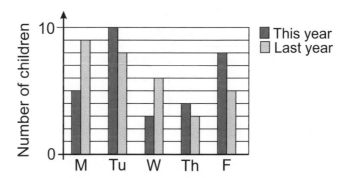

6. How many more children came on the busiest day this year than came on the least busy day last year?

7. Circle the statement below which is not true.

    A   Tuesday is the busiest day this year.

    B   This year, half as many children came on Monday as on Tuesday.

    C   Last year, Monday was three times busier than Thursday.

    D   There were 50% fewer children on Wednesday this year than last year.

    E   There were more children in total this year than last year.

Farmer Grey only has pigs and cows on his farm.

8. Farmer Grey counts his animals and finds there are 10 more pigs than cows, and 58 animals in total. Circle the number of pigs from the options below.

    A   20   **C**   30   **E**   48
    B   24   **D**   34

9. Farmer Grey counts the animals a few months later.
    The number of pigs has doubled.
    The number of cows has increased by $\frac{1}{3}$.
    How many more pigs are there than cows now?

10. Find the value of a in the diagram below.

□□□°

11. Janice wants to buy a new TV. 5 shops have the same TV on sale.
The original price and discount at each shop are shown in the table below.

Circle the shop where Janice can
buy a TV for the cheapest price.

A   TV World
B   Telly City
C   Digi-District
D   Technoland
E   Electromarket

Shop	Price	Discount
TV World	£2000	30% off
Telly City	£1800	25% off
Digi-District	£1600	£150
Technoland	£2100	$\frac{1}{3}$ off
Electromarket	£1500	£80 off

12. The Translator translates a point with given coordinates by a certain
number of units horizontally and vertically, as shown below.

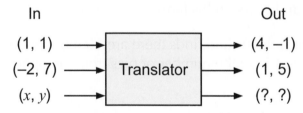

When the point (x, y) goes into the translator, what point comes out?
Circle the correct answer.

A $(4x, -y)$
B $(4x, y - 2)$
C $(x + 3, -y)$
D $(x + 3, y - 2)$
E $(x - 3, y + 2)$

/ 12

You have **10 minutes** to do this test. Work as quickly and accurately as you can.

1. 1 kg of strawberries costs £6.50. Leona buys 100 g of strawberries.
    How much does she pay?

The graph below shows how the temperature inside
a freezer changes after it has been switched on.

2. After how long does the temperature reach 0 °C?
    Circle the correct option.

    A   8 mins 30 secs   **C**   9 mins 30 secs   **E**   10 mins 30 secs

    B   9 mins   **D**   10 mins

3. To the nearest °C, how much has the temperature decreased
    over the 16 minutes shown?

  °C

4. A diagram of a cube and a cuboid are shown below.
    The cube and cuboid have the same volume.
    What is the height of the cuboid?

5. A sequence starts at 32. Each term in the sequence is half of the previous term. Which term in the sequence is the first to have a value that is not a whole number? Circle the correct option.

   A 4th   **B** 5th   **C** 6th   **D** 7th   **E** 8th

6. Jakub arranges 6 candles along the length of a shelf.
   Each candle has a diameter of 38 mm.
   There is a 15 mm space between neighbouring candles.

   How long is the shelf in mm?

   ☐☐☐ mm

A florist has 300 bouquets of roses. 20% are pink bouquets, 60% are red bouquets, 15 are white bouquets and the rest are yellow bouquets.

7. How many of the bouquets are yellow?

   ☐☐

8. Each bouquet has 12 roses.
   How many pink and white roses are there in total?

   ☐☐☐☐

9. What is 685 in Roman numerals? Circle the correct option.

   A CDLXXV   **C** DCLXXXIIIII   **E** DCLXXXV
   B DCXIIIV   **D** LXXXDCV

10. Circle the statement below which is incorrect.

    A   0.05 is equivalent to $^1/_{20}$
    B $^3/_5$ is equivalent to 60%
    C   36.6% is equivalent to 3.66
    D   0.7 is equivalent to 70%
    E $1^1/_4$ is equivalent to 1.25

11. Emma draws the design below.
    The design is made up of a rectangle which contains 4 shaded triangles.
    Each shaded triangle is the same size and shape.

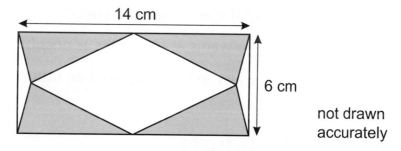

14 cm

6 cm

not drawn
accurately

    What is the total area of the four shaded triangles?

 cm²

12. The mean of three numbers is m.
    Which of the following could be the three numbers?
    Circle the correct option.

    A m, $2m$ and $3m$
    B $m - 2$, m and m
    C $^1/_3 m$, $^1/_3 m$ and $^1/_3 m$
    D $m - 5$, $m + 2$ and $m + 3$
    E $m - 1$, $2m$ and $m + 1$

/ 12

99

Test 31

Now for a break from 10-minute tests. Try out your skills on these puzzles.

Funny Money

In Clown Town, different items are used instead of money to buy things.

The exchange rate for these items is shown on the right.

1 nose = £1	1 flower = £2.50	1 horn = £6.50

Daisy is visiting Clown Town. She goes to the bank to exchange her holiday money (£100) for the items she can spend.

Daisy only has a small bag, so wants as few items as possible.

What should the bank give Daisy in exchange for her £100?

Painting By Numbers

One corner of the grid below contains numbers. If the number in a box is either square, cube or prime, then shade the box. Otherwise leave it unshaded.

6	14	18	24	32	3	35	28	8	20
15	10	40	45	4	21	2	46	52	7
34	48	12	16	51	30	54	17	38	9
50	13	23	56	22	27	57	58	5	11
29	33	42	55	19	39	25	44	26	1

To complete the pattern, shade boxes throughout the whole grid so that the dotted lines are lines of symmetry for the whole pattern.

M6XPD2E1